C000255858

TEGN

Book Three

by Even Mehl Amundsen

To all who are coming along for the journey,
this book is for you

Sytrka

Birker was in a black mood, and in the failing light he could do little but droop in the saddle and brood over how the machinations of the world had led him right back to the same war-weary lands he had given his best year to and had not thought to see again.

The years in the Ram's Guard had been the adventure of his young life, full of the glorious and wild stories that all dwarves want to be able to recount in their cups. Most only serve for a score of years, getting their blooding and some experience to speak of before they are called

back to their clans, or to other frontiers. It had not been so for the White Ram.

His memories were now thick with those later years, with the bitter loss of brothers in arms, of the blood and pain and sacrifice the life demanded, and how no proper payment for it was ever made.

So deep was he in his whirling recollections that he did not even sense her, and he startled as the young voice tore the silence apart, "The White Ram, riding with no eyes, and no ears... you got old!"

The sun was long gone by the time the two riders entered the defile that led to the hidden south gate. They had been spotted a few miles away, and the sparrows had arrived to alert Tuir and his dozen, who had the watch.

Scattered along the approach, they were all hidden and to the unsuspecting eye they were so many rocks that the riders passed them one after the other as they made their way towards the gate. Tuir knew the younger one by sight

if not by sound, for they rode in silence, as any thinking traveller did after dark. No point risking the ears of grey-skin raiders in the foothills. Only as they stopped at the gate did Tuir give himself away, rising up to greet Sytrka with a curt nod, and flashing his lamp towards the trio that followed her. An odd assembly, he thought to himself, and took a step forward, a little suspicious.

"So, who have we here, then?"

Mott

His candles were all burnt down to stubs, save for one, and by its guttering light **Mott** was doing the last of that day's sums, counting up the harvests that had come in and the payments from the treasuries that went to the filling of the winter larders.

The book of records was almost filled and would need be sent off to the Keeper of Tomes at the Red Hold, where the great archives were held, a collection of knowledge and ancient wisdom as valuable as any hording of gold or precious stones, and perhaps the only thing his kind loved better. There were those who would gladly spend an entire life there, among the volumes. He straightened suddenly, the sound of footfalls and the jangling of scaled metal. The guards were always easy to pick out. But what did they want with him?

A red shadow slid in the door and was happily yipping at **Mott** before the rest of them came across the threshold. The guards, who he'd been expecting to summon him brusquely for some audience or another, stayed outside but ushered in a figure that mostly resembled a large bush.

He tucked the quill away, and in the poor light of his candle he began to recognize the features within the foliage.

"Surely not!" He pretended to be talking to Mickel, "What are you still doing lugging this old corpse around?"

The grin on Birker's face was proof enough that for all the changes he could see in him, the old Ram was still the same.

Iron Monger

The clanging of hammers and the squealing of the crafty little grey-skins filled the tumbled down halls of his palace. Once this had belonged to the feeble people, those gentle, pathetic creatures, before they had left it a ruin and the little grey ones had settled the remains. When his throng had come upon them, it had not taken more than the squashing of their little king and his crazed protectors to make them fall in line.

In spite of their frailties and lack of anything approaching courage, his new minions were not entirely without their use. Whenever they had descended from their stronghold to raid and take spoils, a trail of the little ones had followed and, without being asked, would begin hauling the takings back. It was also they who had begun to craft his hard skin. With pieces of iron from all they felled, the grey buggers tore, scrapped, bent and cracked pieces until they got what was needed and fitted them with bolts and ropes and whatever else they could find. For the most part it held together, and if some should chance to fall off, they would use more bolts the next time.

The Sparrows

The Feyr were the smallest of the Tussir folk, the underfoot dwellers, those who live out of sight and are seldom minded, unless they chance to be glimpsed, and even then, for but a second. From unseen vantage, they keep an eye upon the goings-on of the world, for their kind is wide-spread and are fiercely loyal once a friendship is made.

Their appearance is that of a slight person, no taller than the finger of a grown man, but with large, translucent ears that at a glance can be mistaken for wings. All their clothing is made from what the forest provides, and so woven strands of grass, flowers and vines feature often.

For the making of war they have little love, but offer freely to aid the efforts of others. Their love lies in the playing of tricks, the making of music, and the making of mischief. They are like children amongst the green.

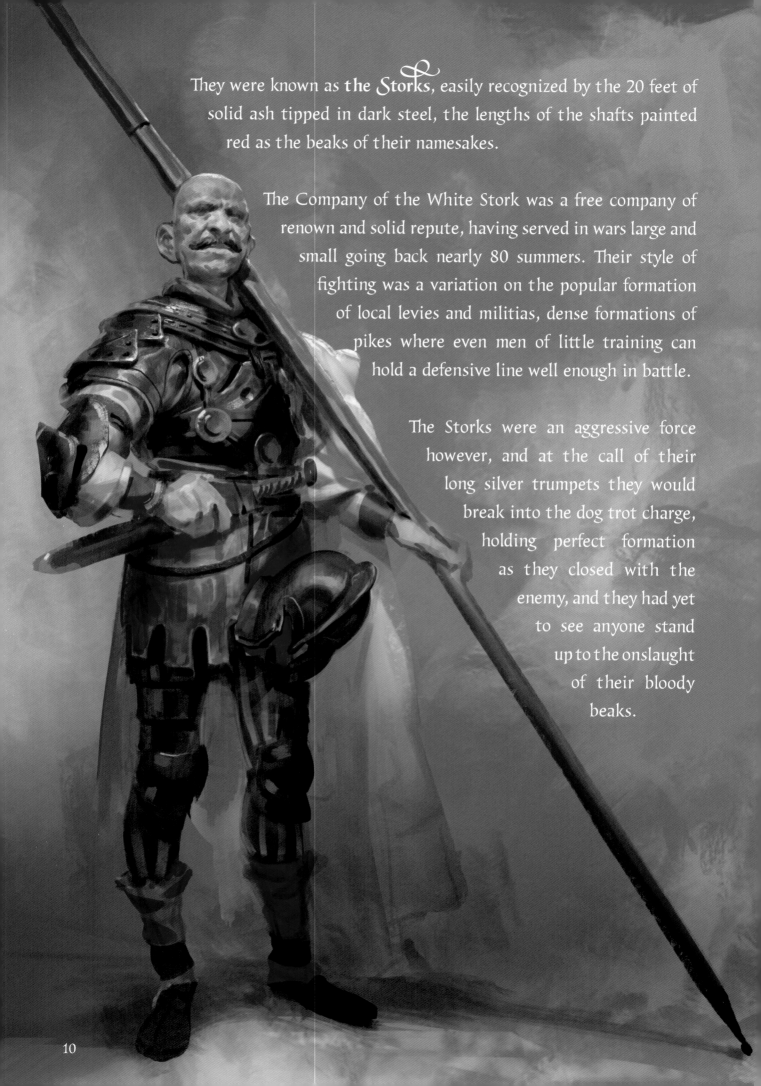

They were known as **the Storks**, easily recognized by the 20 feet of solid ash tipped in dark steel, the lengths of the shafts painted red as the beaks of their namesakes.

The Company of the White Stork was a free company of renown and solid repute, having served in wars large and small going back nearly 80 summers. Their style of fighting was a variation on the popular formation of local levies and militias, dense formations of pikes where even men of little training can hold a defensive line well enough in battle.

The Storks were an aggressive force however, and at the call of their long silver trumpets they would break into the dog trot charge, holding perfect formation as they closed with the enemy, and they had yet to see anyone stand up to the onslaught of their bloody beaks.

Carya bloody well hated taverns. Bloody loud, bloody smelly and unrelentingly bloody populated, they were the kind of place she went adventuring to get away from, and each hour spent waiting by the hearth was a new grudge to wear at her bloody mood.

The elf had paid up front, good solid silver, and had promised twice the sum again at the end of their venture if it turned out well. She was not usually all that greedy for the clink of coin, but with the amount promised she might even buy herself a new horse, and then there was no saying where she might go.

She spat in the fire and considered spending a copper on some of the cat piss that they served up as ale around here. If nothing else, it would pass the time. Half way to calling for the servant girl, she stopped. She had not seen the cold-eyed bastard, but the smell was unmistakable...

His odor was that of heavy, syrupy decay, choking, rather than cutting through, the smell of stale drink and unwashed flesh. The air of effortless superiority was almost as heavy on him, almost as if his first word had been "pleb" and every movement was a lazy, disinterested sweep.

He bid her sit at a table set apart from the crowd in a small alcove, and the barmaid poured their wine before retreating like some terrified rodent scurrying away from a distracted fox. From his pipe emanated sweet tendrils of fragrant smoke, with a scent closer to incense than pipe weed, and for a long while he just watched her, his curious eyes sparkling. When at last he spoke, the words came in a slow, sweet, silvery voice, almost friendly, but friendly in a way where you can just tell that it took a lot of practice. She suppressed a shudder, reminding herself of the money.

"I have use for the particular skillset that someone of your...background... might provide. There is a certain sword of esteemed providence. A sword which is very valuable to me for...sentimental reasons. I want you to help me...retrieve it."

The last couple of words lingered in the air, like so much smoke.

His droning went on, his tales and promises flowing honey-sweet through the smoke and the low murmur of the room and all she need do was listen and wait. She paid little attention to what he said, his words less important than how he said them, and also by what he was avoiding to say. As he came to silence at last, he leaned back and looked down his nose at her, clearly expecting his smooth words to have seduced her into submission. She saw no reason to play this game with him; she was eager to get to the point and get started.

"I will take your coin and do your bidding. The task seems fair enough." His smile slithered wider across his face, and she paused, not able to resist the chance at pricking his cool demeanor. "But when the sword is yours, I will have twice the pay you offered. That is the price of the secret you want kept."

Carÿa rose, nodded, and left him to come to a decision, a sudden furious billow of smoke escaping from his nostrils.

Morstang

The sheets of rain washed across the wetlands, the wind coming in hard over the flats, making the reeds dance and drum against each other, and **Morstang** could sense a change in the weather, the warmth of summer giving way to a dream of fall.

He was looking forward to the wet season, to the cooler months before the winter's storms would set in. The fields would flood then, and bring the fishing closer to home, and the animals who had spent a summer fattening themselves among the grasses would make for good sport. And of course, there would be the feasts.

Ildvin's long strides were gentle as they moved to their last fishing spot for the evening, and he readied the lantern and saw with a smile that there would be tallow to spare for after. The little ones would shout in delight to see the light dancing in the sky as they came flying home.

14

The Chief

He had been against the joining of the clans from the beginning. Young love aside, he saw no good reason to allow those bleedin' mine dwellers to be in charge. Not that he did not fancy a good excavation himself, but there were other things in life, as well...

They had ridden for the better part of two weeks, leaving only they beardlings and the recruits back to hold the keep while the power of the **Duloch Clan** went to feast and prove themselves in the games that would follow the nuptials.

Still, he had to admit, his doubts came from his adherence to the old ways. They had worked for his fathers, and their fathers before them, and he saw it as a small betrayal to them to venture down these new paths. Still, life found strange ways to change things; all a dwarf could do was make the best of it.

Unicorn

The unicorns are rare now, their kind living spread across the lands, the great flocks a thing of the distant past. But once a year they come together for the foaling season. Hidden away from the world, they gather to welcome the new ones in, and to share in the happenings of the year gone by.

These are precious days, a moment of light against a darkening world. Days to keep their dreams alive for another winter.

Univern

A single screech rings out across the valley and a hundred wings and a hundred again rustle and unfold, eyes glint against the first lances of light to break across the dark ridges. Morning has come, and the flocks are on the move.

They cross the lands as a great dark cloud, from which small black shapes detach themselves to plummet and dive, silhouetted against the blue, to take prey, or to savage one another in the play of the young, sometimes as duels, others as full melees, like wild screaming storms.

In their wake a deep silence lies oppressively over the land, nothing moves, nothing stirs, not for hours after. It is as if even the most impetuous animals know that the shadows might return, and that to be in the open is to invite swift, swooping death.

The Bourgermester

Sitting in judgement was one of those things that the **Bourgermester** detested, not only for his distrust of the other judges and those who brought their cases to his court for justice, but also because he was never quite sure how fair one man could be.

He was known to be harsh, yet fair, and would not blink at sending a man to the gallows for murder or ordering a hand or a foot removed, depending on the crime, even if it should be someone he knew. When he sat the bench and held the gavel, he was not just the man that so many called friend, he was what passed for justice personified.

As the next case was prepared and the new petitioners filed into the hall, he shook himself from his thoughts. One man might not be able to be perfectly fair, but as things stood, his own judgement would have to do.

The Squire

The cleaver was a good weapon for a **squire**, sturdy enough to use to fend off attackers, and heavy enough to break bones, even if it did not cut through armor. Where it excelled was at dispatching the foes that Ser Wollam left in his wake as he advanced over the battlefield. As he went to seek more glory, it fell to her to cut the screams and groans and suffering short.

She had not expected it to be so much like butcher's work, when she took the aging knight's coin and signed on as his squire and herald. When she had imagined her time in his service, she had seen herself standing tall, the crowds hanging on her every word as she moved them to cheer and clamor for the Knight of Goltlief.

Still, it was a better life than staying in the comfort of the village, working the gardens and waiting for the next spring fair. While the harvest she now tended was somewhat bloodier, with every mustering, with every battle line, with every swing of the cleaver, she came a little closer to earning her spurs and raising her own banner.

The swamp lands between the outlying villages were the part of her voyage she dreaded the most every time. She always delayed until the dry season was at its peak before she braved the stinking bogs, for while the flies would be swarming thicker with the heat, she was less likely to be stuck in the muddy expanses.

It was the smell that made the worst of it, the mixing of decay, wet rot, and slow death could sap her will over the days, so much so that sometimes she needed a few days to regain her strength once she reached a village. But as she came back to herself, she went about her duties, lancing boils, making ointments, and tending to all the little wounds that were unavoidable in the rough lives of the badlands.

The Healer

The cool evening air felt good after the torrent of the days worked had worn down to a trickle and she could retreat to the shade of the trees and rinse her hands of the sticky blood that covered her almost to the elbow. She had been at it for almost two days at this point.

She had met the hunting party as they departed, a throng of hounds and men hurrying out as the word had passed that a herd of elk was coming through their woods. She had known then that there would be bloody work and had begun preparing, even before the normal chores had been tended to.

They had heard the first of the wounded long before they saw them, carried by their comrades as their lives rushed away in great crimson heaves. By sunset, she had stitched more than a dozen, and only one of them had slipped away from her. She took pride in days like these.

Queen of Autumn

With the closing of the harvest came the autumn market, and from all around came the spoils of the year's toil, golden fruits piled high, roots and vegetables, and all that which the earth had yielded. Meat, too, was brought out, some from fresh butcheries, some the cured meats from the years past, seasoned with the passing of time.

The high point of the market would be the fair, a great feast of three full days where gifts were exchanged, games were played large and small, and there was music and dancing and all the rest that comes with it. At the height of it all would be the crowning of the **Queen of Autumn**, one of the young women to stand as the harvest goddess in effigy.

It always ended with a procession, and the queen would be carried aloft through the crowded streets, lauded with flowers and cheers. She would have songs sung to her, and many would be the young man who would try for her attentions, though it was seldom that anyone got to become king.

22

Blomst

"Here, a small gift from us to you from us to you." The kindness came as if whispered, making the old man startle out of his thoughts and nearly had him stumble and fall. He regained the vertical and stood staring at the offered token.

The underfootlings had been his unseen friends since he first had settled under the canopies, and while they had only let their presence be known by the occasional pilfered harvest, they would always leave him with something as thanks. Over time they had become his protectors, and unless it was by his own invitation, no one seemed to be able to find their way to his hovel, deep in a copse of trees.

For the first time in a long time, he was venturing out under the blue and he had been worried about leaving the safety of his haven under the trees. The outworld was a dangerous place, but as he touched the offered flower, his gnarled hands grasping it with infinite care, he knew that his friends would be with him, and he smiled in thanks and bowed deeply.

23

The Longstrider

He knew he did not have the swift feet of his youth, speed being something he had abandoned with wisdom and age, but his days of marching to the tune of drums and sergeants had taught him the dogged trot of the veteran soldier.

The sun had little mercy for travellers on the open road, and under her attentions he had soon punished the water skin severely, seeking out any reprieve from the relentless glare, lingering in the shade a little longer each time.

By the time the sun began westering he was all but spent and swore harshly at his loss of stamina. In his young days, he would have put many more miles behind him, and marched on into the witching hour before setting up camp. But he was no longer young...he was old, and he was wise enough to know his limits.

The Plainsfolk

The great grasslands that cover the vale between the Orchenridge Mountains and the broken lands of Uhr are home to an odd breed of the horse people. It is often said that their origin was the love between one of the centaurii and one of the proud chiefs of the Blue Beard Clan, though this is of course nonsense.

While they are smaller than the rest of their kin, stocky of build and stout of heart, they move across the rolling sea of green with great speed and can keep at a pace for longer than most others. They live as a city on the move, their herds eating the grazing to the root before moving on, and they gather in great roaming hordes, their strength and safety being found in their numbers.

As with all of the centaurii, they are a quarrelsome lot, and when an outside enemy is not at hand they will fight each other, as much for the love of battle as for conquest and raiding, but they also have a love for the feast and the drink, and feuds are as often settled by bouts of drinking as bouts of fighting.

Bog Witch

"Don't go beyond the beyond the fog!"

They had been the only words that had passed between them, thrown over a retreating shoulder as the small family and their wagon ambled down the path in a hurry.

He shook his head at the superstitions of peasants and trudged on, set on making it at least another few miles before losing the light. It came creeping along as the shadows lengthened, thick grey tendrils that covered the path and the forest floor, stealing away the colors of the world, and he began regretting not going along with the peasants as he felt the first chill steal over him.

Still, there was no turning back, so he gritted his teeth and resolved to march through it, to not let this laughable mist defeat him, and suddenly he heard the low hiss that froze him in his stride. He turned slowly in the direction of the sound to see a cold gleam of light coming towards him, and as it approached a specter seemed to materialize around it. The scream he wanted to utter seemed to stick in his throat, and all he could do was stand there.

He could not move, he could not scream, he was frozen to the very tips of his fingers, to the very depth of his heart. The ghostly apparition came closer, gliding as if the pull of the ground had no say in the matter

At first it felt like cold, a deep chill stealing in and adding to his helpless condition, then it simply felt like death coming to take him, as if his stolen time had finally run out and now he would have to pay, and as hope was being choked out in front of his eyes, a sudden glimpse of sanctuary.

A glow from above, a faint but solid ember of warmth and light, a halt to the encroaching oblivion. The apparition pulled back and lowered its hood, staring eyeless towards that ember of hope. A simple sentence, a few words of safeguard, "You are protected; you may pass."

Scinna

The blade sang like a silvered whisper on the wind as it slid from the scabbard, the sound of steel on leather bringing a glint of malevolence to her steady stare. Those who thought themselves the ruthless hunters were about to find out what it meant to be prey.

She had been keeping in front of them for eight days, always out of reach, but never so far as to make them give up. She had played her part beautifully, and now they were deep in the trap, though they did not know it yet, but among these standing stones there were none who could even touch her.

They were circling now, thinking themselves strong, like wolves readying themselves for the bloody kill, closing the noose on a skittish doe. Little did they know they were surrounding a monster, ready to turn their illusions into their doom.

Scinna carved them up, one after the other, some with the smooth silvered arcs of her sword as it sliced the air, its heavy blade crushing what it did not cut, others with her dagger making short work of any exposed flesh. Her blood was boiling and the dance became a wild blur.

Some died well, coming at her bravely and going down with a curse as she overcame them, accepting their end at her hand. Others were not so strong, weeping and screaming as she opened them in terrible ways, leaving them holding themselves together as the understanding of their folly came over them.

In the end, there was only one left, the master of the hunt, who had led the pack of dogs from the back, letting them die as he urged them onto her blades. Now he had none left to throw at her, no more gifts for her to accept, and so it was time she offered him her gratitude.

The hogs could always smell it on the wind when the butchering day was coming around. They would be jumpy at first, distrustful when they knew something was afoot, but as the nervous energy wore off they would become brooding and angry, biting and pushing at anyone who came within reach, attempting to intimidate.

When the day came, however, they would have no nerve left. Their strength, their frustration, and anger were spent against their confinement and at last broken against their bondage, and all that was left was a resignation to their demise. They all still squealed at the end though, a horrible, sad sound of pity and anguish as the beast saw its end.

The master of the hunt had been like one of the big, fat hogs, all loud snorts and bulk, all headstrong bullying. As the knife came out though, he had squealed like all the rest of them, begging and groveling, snarling and sniveling. He bled like a hog as well, and the dying crimson stained the standing stones, seeped into the soil, and renewed the power of the great carved circle.

The **hunters** could trace their tales in the scars that crisscrossed their bodies, telling of the hot-blooded chases, the desperate struggles and the savage satisfaction at bringing down the great beasts in the forest. All the things that attracted the select few to the life of the hunt.

Returning to the huts always became an occasion of a feast, glad reunions after weeks and months apart from their kin, and new stories to tell, and old stories to be recounted by the bajama, the wise old lady. It was a hard life, sometimes a brutal one, but Parchee knew it was a good one.

The glint in **Røys'** eye held **Spiss'** gaze for a long moment. Last night, it had inspired the confidence to get him to come along on this adventure, but now, standing by the crumbling corner stones of the tower, he had a sudden, clear grasp of his position in the world and how tiny that position was.

"Come off it, ye toothy git, if we end up standin' round here all night some owl is gonna spot us and we'll be about as heroic as a midnight snack." The mention of the winged death made Spiss look around, his eyes darting from side to side, looking for monsters among the dark trees.

All the stories that had been told to him, from the pile where he grew up to the Needle's Eye only a few hours before, had all told of the bravery of heroes, of their exploits and adventures. The struggle of taking the first step, though, they had always glossed over that part. He wiggled his, he tightened his grip on his dagger, and he overcame.

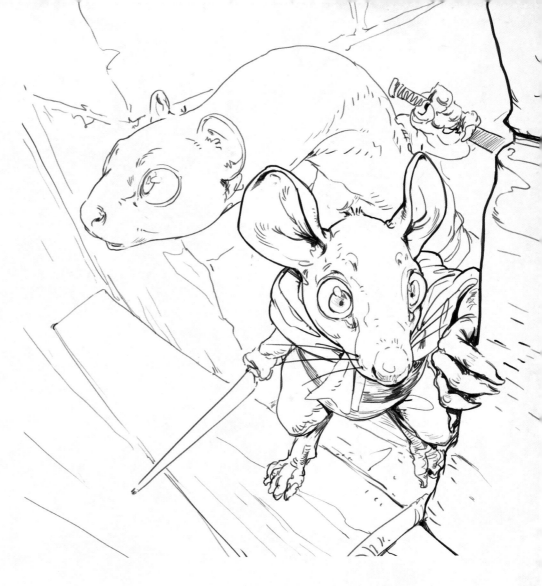

The pitter patter of the footfalls rang like the beating of war drums in their ears, the silence of the dark being a solid nothingness only broken by the heart-stopping sound of a drop of water falling from on high to dash upon the unmortared rocks that built the ancient keep.

Holes and crevices were everywhere, for while the walls were solid and sturdy, they were not impervious to the intrepid explorations of their kind, nor to the wear and tear of time, and so they found their way inside the walls, over rafters and under floors, climbing ever higher.

The silence became a low murmur, the murmur became a jumble of sounds, and the more they climbed, the more each sound became more distinct, but more importantly to them, they began to pick up the faint, wafting scents of the food. Soon they found an opening onto a beam up under the ceiling of a large room and peeked out, their eyes darting here and there, looking for the looming shape of a guarding predator. After being satisfied that they were not about to become lunch themselves, they took in the room and suddenly saw where the delicious smells had come from.

Taking in the sight of great platters of sweet meat being prepared over the roaring fires, and the heaps of other foods laying piled on boards and plates, their stomachs growled alarmingly, and Spiss merely needed to look over to know what was in Røys' mind.

With all the food these dwarves had hoarded in their larder, it did not feel like such a monstrous crime to lift a cut of the great wheels of cheese and a few of the fat sausages that hung from the rafters enticing the little adventurers with their scent. The cooks would be none the wiser.

Safely up under the ceiling again, well-hidden by the billowing steam of the kitchen below, they felt rather better about their quest. Already they had spoils, and that first bite of the cheese put a pep in Spiss' step. Let the adventure go ahead!

Their looted morsels were gone to the last bite, tasting all the better for the dangers they had risked to get them, and filled with that glee of fools and heroes, they continued their climb, passing again into the maze inside the stonework walls.

As the noises of the kitchens receded under them and the smells of delicious food no longer overpowered their senses, they picked up other scents from the rooms they passed. A smell of steel and oil gave them the guard room, and the stink of bodies gave them the bunk room, though in truth the sound gave it away before the smell.

The odd smell of something they could not place was what drew them back towards the open, and the risk of light. They could hear two voices laughing and talking, the clink of pewter and the pouring and sloshing of drink. It was the sudden appearance of a smell that ought not be there that made them turn, and instantly regret the entire undertaking.

Spiss and Røys

The ale was sweet on the tongue, but heady and strong, and with the haze of his pipe Birker was well-settled in happy reminiscences of old adventures once more, helped along with Mott's telling of the happenings along the borderlands, of the new bands formed under the Ram's Guard banner, and the comings and goings of friends of old.

Slowly a map was forming in his head of where the road now lay ahead, what keeps could be counted on, and which would need convincing. It would be no easy task, and even if he could gather the entire guard, as in the days of old, it might still not be enough to do what needed to be done.

It was a balm to his troubles to hear the careless, happy "yipp, yipp, yipp" of Mickel who had seen fit to leave the comfort of Mott's lap and was busy doing the duty traditionally reserved for the cats of the keep, chasing around the room like a slippery, orange blur.

Myri loved fall the best of all. The rain chasing her on wild flights from cover to cover in a breathless storm of movement, the trees afire with a hundred shades of reds and a hundred again, and the autumn wind, her fiercest friend. Never was she as free as when the gusts took ahold and carried with them the dream of the clean cold of winter, and the promise of spring anew. The best thing of all, was that fall was hers and hers alone, and while others cursed the rain and fled the wind and saw the leaves as just another chore to be cleaned away, she would sing wildly, and for a glorious few weeks she would be happy.

She loved fall best of all, and with such love, she needed no other.

"Old before my time, the fickle winds of the gods will take it all in the end."

Tinura had but a dozen summers and a dozen more, but already she could sense the changing of the weather, the coming of the storm, the ending of summer as aches in her bones, as stiff joints and weariness. Still, she had her mind, she had her ways, she had her powers, and she still had her mind, or so she reasoned, as she could still think circles around anyone else from the village, best them all in any game of wits or chance, and the last laugh was forever hers.

Yes, she still had her mind, her truest friend...her mind...it would be the last that would be taken from her...

Black Mountains

The migration of the clans back towards the **Black Mountains** was the beginning of the end of each season. Hunters from each great banner would gather in large parties and scour the plains clean of wildlife, consuming a year's supply of salt and great clouds of smoke to have the meat keep over the winter that would soon descend.

Droves of elk made up the heart of the horde as they moved, a city crossing the open lands, unhalting, always between resting places but still alive with all the crafts and arts of their cousins of stone. Where other cities had walls, this one was encircled by the sweeping forms of riders and steeds keeping their eyes on the horizon. In the bosom of the holy mountain, they would spend the winter, raising the new foals that had joined the herds, training the new warriors, gathering for the feast of the Allnight, after which the chiefs would compete for the election of the Black Crown. Then the year would start anew, and once again, the people would move.

Silk Spinners

The **silk makers** among the Deep Elves are not like the cloth makers among any other peoples of the known world. Where others spin thread and weave cloth from their animals and plants, keeping great herds and fields, the forest dwellers go about their craft with somewhat more of a seductive approach.

It begins, like any craft among their kind, in the sproutling years, where those with the aptitude will begin to attract the spinners, their name for the silks spiders of the Deep Woods, and train them to spin their silk better suited for clothing than hunting. In return, the spinners are allowed refuge and protection by the young ones. Some even manage to shape their growers into a nest for their new familiars.

As their grow and improve their craft, their control of the spinners increases to where they can have them spin patterns, and some even feed them separately so the coloring of their silk is altered. No silk is stronger, lighter or finer than that spun by the elves of the Deep Woods, not since the days of the Kingdoms of Old.

"Child, for why did they give you to me?"

"For this, child, for this you were given to my tutelage."

It was phrased as a question, but all in the room knew the trap, and none volunteered an answer, most of all the sproutling who suffered under that cold yellow gaze.

Even as she sat still she was dominant, a pool of stillness in a great scurrying of black shapes and a thousand little legs hurrying to and fro, spinning their threads, all running through her control, a queen of spinners indeed. She allowed the silence to run a little longer, before she leaned forward and beckoned for the approach. The timid footfalls came one after the other, and when she was close enough for a whisper to suffice, the answer came as a hiss.

The older arm reached out, a single finger extending towards the squirming sproutling at the center of attention. Along the extremity darted forward a small black shape, weaving a way along the grower roots until it reached the hand, the knuckles, and out along the finger.

A trembling hand reached up, not so frightened at the teetering creature, feelers outstretched searching, but trembling at the eyes so far behind, looking. Eyes locked, yellow on yellow, and the hand steadied as little legs took their first, unsure steps onto new ground.

This is how they all start, the silk makers, with a first contact, with an acceptance, and a bond as strong as silk. The shadow of a smile wisped across the face behind the outstretched arm, looking upon the making of a new covenant.

Black Arrows

They were calling every last man out now to join the militia and hold for one last desperate fight. *Scutt* counted his arrows, four and ten shafts left. Worn, but well-made, they would have a few more of the raiders bleeding before night fell.

He had been in apprenticeship with the lodge for three seasons now but had only taken his first kill from stalk to blood this past year, and he could still remember the warm sticky blood on his cheeks, the blood of the wolf mixing with the red stream leaking from his cuts.

Yet, for all the curiosity of the wolf, killing a man was worse, and none was harder than seeing that first one go down, the broad head of the arrow taking him in the shoulder and driving through, pinning him as he fell to the ground. He had taken to thinking of them as more monsters than men like the ones he stood with; it made it easier to let go of the shaft.

Winter Prayers

The north wind was coming, bringing with it the hold of winter, the warm balm of evening had diminished and the chill had capes being pulled tighter and doors closed to keep the warmth in.

Of the tribes that had made their way to the Black Mountains, only a few would make the climb up the slopes and spend the cold months in the caves, praying and speaking with the gods, offering the gifts of the people to them, learning their wisdom and receiving their bounty.

Even the youngest of those families were to take part. The gift of the Sight seldom crossed bloodlines, though it happened, but the secrets of the gods and their communion was a well-guarded secret, never imparted in whole to any single person. Not for many an age had there been someone so loved by the gods as to wear the Mantle and the Helm, not since the Time of the Songs, and who knows when one might come again.

The Gathered

Hooded and cowled, and oft seen only in the light of the moon and the stars travelling south in spring, the clear nights with the coming of warm and light a fine backdrop for her wanderings, she was travelling north now, making for the White Grove, and the meeting of all her kind.

They were not the carriers of great tomes of spells, nor of the power to wield the elements as weapons, but those who give themselves to all that grows have an older, stronger power at their calling, a power that takes its toll in warm blood. But they must be their full number, and they must act with clarity, with resolve.

Soon she would be joined by others on the journey, and before the moon had come and gone they would reach the grove, and the preparations could begin. As she walked she dreamt of what was to come, and the rustle of the wind and the rhythm of her bell became her marching music.

49

Granny Ponds

She smiled up at Hraban as he poked her, his beak cold against her skin, like the breeze that was slowly dispersing the morning mist. The bog was warm though, under the layers of muck and plants that lay over it like a protective blanket, only moving aside at her passing. All the while, Octua sat proud and high, a queen on her throne.

Names she bestowed on everyone and everything, but kept none for herself, yet had so many given to her. She was the Old Lady of the Mists, the Witch of the Waters, she was **Granny Ponds**, and when the villagers offered her strong drink as thanks for a remedy or a mended wound, the Old Cackler was on hand. But none of these did she keep for herself.

There was no use for it, for she knew herself. Ever since she had been young and beautiful had she known what it was to have something and have no need of it.

She never scorned her suitors, she simply slipped from their grasping efforts and swept herself from their minds. Her being was her own, and not at the bidding of anyone else.

Fear was not new to **Old Granny Ponds**, but it was an acquaintance she had kept at a distance for these many years past. The word was good and doom, and it came on the wind from the north ranges, on hooves and paws and beating wings, and for the first time in a long time she did not know what to do.

She was in her methods as mighty in the disparate ways and winds of magic as anyone who probed and prodded the arcane, but she doubted her abilities would be much use against the cruel means of the oncoming dark. Not for her to dam the flow and be the bulwark upon which the flood would break. This line of persuasion got her almost all the way back to the hut before she shook herself and halted. She leaned on her staff, her head turning this way and that, as if trying to get to two sides of an argument happening only in her own hearing. At last she sighed, as if conceding a point and her shoulders sagged.

"Very well,"
the words laced with exasperation,
"let us go see the iron-fanciers."

Tuquagi Axes

The moon had died and come anew four times since the lonely rider had come in from the front, the glad tidings that the king's brother and his allies had won a victory. It had come at a heavy cost, but even so it was the will of the court to do great honor upon their glorious champions.

To the City of Readers came every lord and petty king who owed their allegiance from oaths and promises of old, bringing with them their retinues, their scribes and underlings, and bodyguards made up of all sorts of warriors, and the people of the city took pride in seeing the might of their king displayed.

Of the first to arrive at court were the **Tuqagi**, led by their queen and the ladies of her court. It was a jest of sorts, her retinue of ladies, for they were all big in build, lithe of muscle, carrying great axes, and well-known for fearing no man. They did not march, unlike most other soldiers, rather they surrounded their queen, moving with the grace of the great cats of their homeland, only parting to let their sovereign approach the Reader's Throne.

53

The Silken Spears

Like whirling storms of silk did they enter the great hall of court, a torrent of spinning, leaping, twirling shapes, trailing long bands of silk that hung in the air after them, only to be snapped on by the next explosive hurl of their beings. They carried broad bladed spears that spun and flashed in step with their wielders.

At some silent signal, the wild dances came to a stop, each guard in an elegant kneel, side by side in straight rows down the length of the hall, their weapons upraised to form an honor guard for the one they had all sworn their lives to protect.

An imposing figure, a head taller than any man in the court, stepped in through the doors, only just passing without having to incline his head, and began a procession towards the throne, seeming to carry a burden in powerful arms. The hangings of silk and embroidered cloth gave the distinct impression of a dignitary, rather than a ruler.

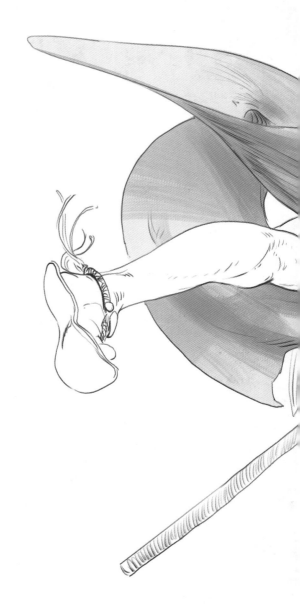

As the towering figure neared the throne it became clear it was merely a beast of burden, a giant compared to any man, but willingly steered by the slight figure of the **Petal Princess** seated on a cushion securely held in hands as large as plates.

In a single motion, fluent and not without elegance, the giant kneeled before the court, holding the queen aloft, perfectly balanced on her throne of velvet and tassels. She spoke in a singsong voice, with the arrogance that only nobility can masquerade for humility.

For all it was a posture and a show, no one would deny the beauty of it, and a roiling tribute of clapping hands and fawning compliments was showered upon her as the queen took her place beneath the throne.

The merchant princes arrived in great splendor, clad in the silks and fine fabrics from far afield, and chiming with the hangings of many metals and precious stones.

These men, whose forefathers had been the great warlords of the dry, red deserts, had grown monstrously rich by securing and partaking in the trade that now flowed to and from Sarn Qorn and her sister cities.

Where the people of the dunes once fought their battles with swords and spears and wild cries of bravery, these men had become masters of intrigue, and were all of them continuously embroiled in an intricate game of power, a game that only stopped at the threshold of the High Reader's city, for they all recognized him as overlord and accepted his rules and his protection.

Xamophon

The last host of guests to be presented before the court wore more riches on their heads than all the others gathered together. Their guards wore burnished scales and helms, resplendent in the light of a thousand candles, but the three at the core of that laden throng stood out and stood forth.

It was impossible to mistake the leader, Xamophon of the Golden Hoard, who was clad in gold of all shades, and all from the rich seams of his mountain

kingdom. Old gold, yellow gold, red and white gold, set off against the gleam of his oiled black beard and the iron cloth of his garb.

He was a proud lord of a people quick to insult and long in anger and wrath, but even admitted the debt that was owed the slight figure who gestured a welcome from the high seat. Even in a bow, a dwarf will not bend the knee, for it is to them a gesture of deepest respect but not of subservience.

Ragnhild

The bog steel sang under the dark stone as **Ragnhild** pulled it along the length of the blade, the sweet sound winding its way down the length of the ship, and mingling with the banter, the chatter and the steady rhythm of the oars. It was late in the year to be going out, but as the captain ordered, so did the crew oblige.

Gone was her fine raiment, packed away in safe keeping with her family, and donned was gear more suitable to the travels ahead. The ringmail was another fine gift of her father's forge, well-suited to her way of fighting. The arrows and daggers that might pose her a threat she would defeat with speed, and the thick iron rings would put a stopper to anything much larger.

The edge was now so sharp, she was sure even gods would think twice before getting on her wrong side. Now for the oilcloth, and the sheath, then it would be her turn at the oars. She knew she would have to steel herself against the jests and barbs Tyrev would be flinging her way, but smiled, not hating that prospect altogether.

Rolf had good fingers for braiding; though coarse from the hours spent with ropes and arms, they were nimble, and he knew the art well. **Ragnhild** loved the freedom of unbound hair, but it was not good now that there had been a call for scouts to go out and go ahead of the ships.

They had been holding a course east for almost a week, the wind carrying their ships swiftly over rough autumn seas, staying out of sight of land for the most part. They wanted to go unseen and took the risk of weathering the wind.

It was all hands to the oars once they set the course for the mouth of the river, the grand waterway where rivers beyond counting finally found their way out to sea. This would be their path further inland than anyone had gone before them, for Harl had plans greater than mere raids.

What time they had for hunting and gathering was scarce, having to keep ahead of the ships, but the lands were rich, and simply passing through was hard for the northerners.

Ragnhild had been keeping an eye on this prize for a few days now, noting how lesser beasts were sacrificed for its survival, but the crowned leader would always make a show of protecting his wounded brethren. Pride. It was always a weakness, and she would wield it as any other weapon, and find a way to strike at the heart of the flock.

Only four shafts remained to her as the shadows began to lengthen, and still, she went on. She had scoffed at the pride that caused such folly in others but had to chuckle at the fine line between that curse and her own stubbornness so fierce she would continue the hunt long after everyone else had returned to the river. The woods here were different from the ones she was used to, lighter somehow, with a riot of colors in the afternoon light, a spectacle through which she stalked like death on silent feet, her every sense tensed and tuned to the betrayal of her quarry's presence.

The stiff hairs of the feathers rustled gently against her finger as she chose a shaft, easing it from the quiver. The quiet of the woods was now so complete, even the birds had quieted their song and were still, and a thought that she might have been led came to the fore of her mind.

She spun at the sound that she recognized as a muffled giggle only as **Ragnhild** had her bow at full draw. The movement had been fluid and perfect, yet where she expected the fletching of the arrow to tickle her cheek, there was nothing. Her hand closed on empty air when she reached for another arrow, and she would have been surprised, but she saw where they had all gone in that same moment. Grinning past the arrow in her teeth, the creature had somehow lifted not only her arrows, but the fine sword from her father's forge. It stunned her, the thought that anyone could have taken her so unaware, especially someone so ridiculous. She sighed.

"You're a god, aren't you?" her tone one of exasperation rather than awe.

The mumbled reply was broken off and resumed as she spat out the arrow. "Clever one! You stalkers always are the clever ones, though not as clever as me!" The cackling laugh was shrill, and filled the clearing, rebounding off of the sheer rock faces all around. "And now, I think I will teach you a lesson, my little hunter."

The **Blackhead** trolls are among the smaller species of trolls, though they do what they can to make up for it by butting heads with anything or anyone who trespasses on their territory. Unlike most trolls, they live in herds and they have even taken to animal husbandry, having made themselves the masters of the highland musk oxen the same way they fight everyone else. The larger of the warlords have even managed to become adept riders of the shaggy beasts.

They are fiercely independent and make great shows of protecting and strengthening their clans, so much so that when they lack an exterior enemy, the clans will fight each other, and so their warriors are well-seasoned in war.

Nayimeq had always wanted to see the gathering of the banners, see them born forth at the head of the great war hosts that each of the realms could field, see the champions of his people call up the glory of the days of old. Seeing it all at last, he was all the more awed, for though yet not blooded, he was a warrior, eager to show his mettle.

Like a forest moving within a forest, they were travelling under the cover of the leaves as far as they could, their eyes out to all directions, on fleet feet and swift wings, and no enemy would know that they were coming. For a turn of the seasons and half a turn again, the elders had sat in council, while the young had prepared for dark tidings. Though the word was war, it was a relief to be released from the agony of uncertainty.

He heard the summons and rejoined the riders of the column, finding a place

towards the back, and took in the sight of their army on the move once more. To see the sprawling circus of their army was to see the alliances, old and new, that his people so lovingly tended with the land and with their neighbors. A friend who would go with you to war, now there was a fine friend.

The whole of the woodlands was present in the host, from largest to smallest, and while the reassuring bulk of the Keepers rumbled by, it was to the smallest of their growing company that attracted the eyes from the young rider.

Mounted on their largest birds, the **Feyr** were ever at the edges of the moving lines, serving as carriers of important news, as well as eyes to all sides, and could be seen swooping and diving in the delivery of their precious tidings.

It had been a truth told to him long ago, that never would he see the best of his people and his realm until he saw them go to war. To see them all united to one purpose, that was true glory, and his heart swelled with pride at a being among them.

In the midst of the moving mass, untroubled, looming over the rest like boulders in a flowing river, the **Keepers** moved. Not walking or a shuffling, or marching, for that you needed feet. Any of the countless roots and branches that reached the forest floor carried it along, the creaking of wood and the flapping of its streamers accompanying a low murmur that was more felt than heard.

They were the gathering of old magic, were the Keepers, each of them formed around runestones older than the Deeping Kingdom itself, and each of them a terrible sight to behold once battle was joined. No two were alike, though they all bore the striking resemblance of hillocks out for an afternoon stroll.

In the shadow of their protection, there reigned peace even as they were marching off to war, the loudest song that of the birds rather than bravado. Still, it was a solemn march that took them ever closer on, towards the breaking of the calm and the ensuing storm.

As the forest began to climb the side of the mountains, and the craggy hills and outcroppings made an end to the smooth expanse of the forest floor, the hill tribes came to join their banners to the great host, and their voices to the songs of the march.

They were an impetuous folk, and only the call of their king could summon their banners and their swords to any united end, though even before the hosts had joined together, the sounds of horns clashing with horns had echoed through the forest. They were a stubborn lot, and proud. Only one among them had the strength to wrangle them, to master them and to turn them to his bidding. Only one had the standing, and the right, bought dearly, a cost of blood and years and toil. He bore it as a privilege, an honor well-deserved, and where he went they followed willingly.

It was said they could live off of the barren mountainside itself, chewing the very rocks for food, with no fear of wind and weather, and no need for shelter from even the cruelest storm. To have such folk as brothers in battle was to lift the hearts of everyone on the march.

In truth, the **satyrii** are great makers of cave dwellings, carving great cities from the very rocks, their facades and livery beautiful to behold. Unlike the dwarves, they have no interest in tunneling and mining, and prefer the wind and the sun of the high places and are almost as hardy as they would have us all believe.

While those marching with the great woodland host were a broad swathe of the mountain-dwelling clans, there are others who have settled in other places, far from the cold winds and snows. The woods, the hills, and even the deserts have been known to be home to the satyrii.

71

Carya

When the first sword came swinging, **Carya** had grinned in the dark, her torch flung aside as her blade slid from the scabbard, and a moment later the harsh clang of iron blades filled the cavernous tunnel, echoing off the walls and drowning out the grunts of men going down.

The explosion of violence was a relief to her; she had no patience for sneaking around in the dark. Her shoulders always tingled as if there was someone always at her back, and she had never been much good at being quiet anyway.

He had told her there would be men there, brutal men, serving clever masters, and that to take them unawares would make her task all the easier. But where was the fun in that? These were not the kind of men who would throw down their knives and hatchets, no matter how sweetly she asked, nor would they stand aside if honorably defeated. They spoke only one language, and she was ready for a good quarrel.

It came to daggers in the end. It so often did, and it was always messy.

Her sword had lodged in the shoulder of the fourth man, pulled free of her hands as he fell screaming against a wall, and as she moved out of the way of the next attack, her hand snatched at the hilt hidden under the pelt, bringing it out and around in a short, sharp arc, punching the broad blade into the face of the last man.

Her eyes ran down the jagged edge of her sword, the old iron dark against the blood, the blade seamed and weathered, and yet beautiful to her. A new blade was always a temptation, maybe something lighter, something that would hold the edge better, something that would not demand such close caresses from her whetstone. She shook her head as she sheathed the dagger and began to work the sword free, knowing that such temptations were for others with more gold and less sense. She knew this blade, old, weathered and scarred; Carya knew its weight, its bite, its song. Friends like that were not to be replaced.

73

Steel and flint, steel and flint, never leave home without them. The torch sputtered and hissed as the fresh flame took in the oil-soaked rags, and she stepped over the bodies and descended into the dark. The stale, fettered smell of the stagnant water was far more unpleasant than actually stepping into the muck, but she tried to ignore it as cold fingers worked their way into her wrappings and boots. She would have the bastard pay for a new pair on top of what else he owed her.

The torch gave off just enough light to make the cavern out, a long, narrow room with worn pillars leading down a passage, the flooding having left marks up the walls and the columns, a dark border where the filth had gone no further. Now it lay before her, a smooth, stinking veneer breaking apart before her wading advance. What little noise **Carya** made seemed as loud as a thundering storm next to the nothingness, and the deeper she went the harder it was to avoid imagining you saw something out there in the dark, just at the edge of vision, something moving, but making no sound at all.

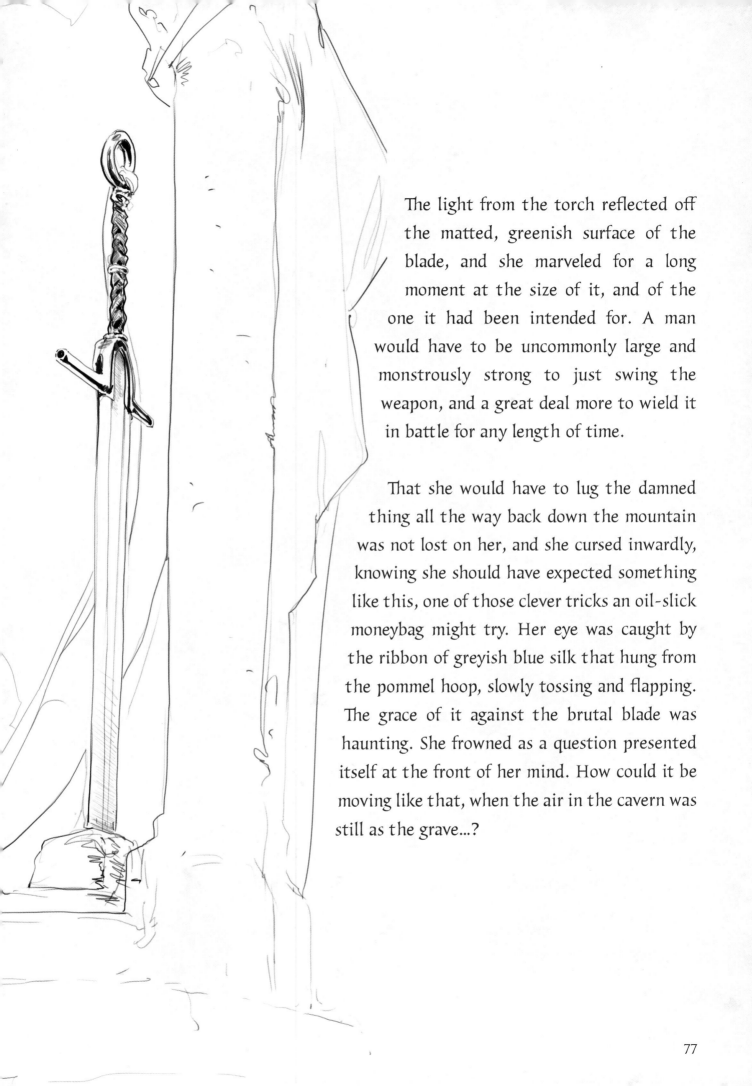

The light from the torch reflected off the matted, greenish surface of the blade, and she marveled for a long moment at the size of it, and of the one it had been intended for. A man would have to be uncommonly large and monstrously strong to just swing the weapon, and a great deal more to wield it in battle for any length of time.

That she would have to lug the damned thing all the way back down the mountain was not lost on her, and she cursed inwardly, knowing she should have expected something like this, one of those clever tricks an oil-slick moneybag might try. Her eye was caught by the ribbon of greyish blue silk that hung from the pommel hoop, slowly tossing and flapping. The grace of it against the brutal blade was haunting. She frowned as a question presented itself at the front of her mind. How could it be moving like that, when the air in the cavern was still as the grave...?

It was as heavy as she had feared and took some wrestling to get free of the plinth before she could hold it and test the weight. With an effort and a grunt, she might be able to swing it, but with the grace and elegance of a ruffled musk ox.

She tugged at the length of cloth hanging from the standing stone, the smooth cloth drifting down to her as it came free of its perch, and she spent some time wrapping the length of the blade before lifting it onto her back and fixing it there.

The torch fizzled out as she let it drop to the damp ground at the bottom of the stairs, hearing the chatter and noise of men moving about outside. They did not seem too troubled about the dead out there, but she did not think them friends. **Carya** crept slowly towards the opening, naked blades in hand, the flicker of fresh flames outside, and she counted them, one after another, swallowing as the count rose above a dozen.

The Beaten

The marshes were quiet, or as quiet as anywhere could be with a few thousand of the grey folk sprawled out on a miserable, little, dry crop surrounded by the stinking bog. Still, there was drink aplenty now that there were fewer mouths to wet, and **Krolg** was happily drunk, which was the only way to be on lookout duty as far as he was concerned.

After the Golden Eyed had been killed, and they had been driven back across the river by the horses and the bows, they had all come to bow to the will of the Hag, the tribe ancient, and mother of mothers. She had taken them north into the mountains and beyond. Many had given up in the high passes, the bite of the wind tearing at their will, and sapping it.

Now they were lost, weak, more like animals in a frightened flight for refuge than a marauding horde, and with the loss of so many chiefs and warlords, many did not know who to follow. Still, there was a lot to drink, Krolg thought happily to himself, and was just about to take another pull at the skin when he heard someone coming and turned to see.

The Broken

Gamiczh snarled as he came up alongside the drunkard Krolg, grabbing the skin of fierce drink and taking a deep swallow before hurling the bloody thing back, catching the lout in the face, his hands coming up far too late, fumbling the catch. He was in a foul mood, still begrudging his being put with the spawn, the drunks, and the dumb on watch duty. That he, who had stood and bled and fought in glorious battle with the Golden Eyed himself should have been brought to this, it was enough to wake the wrathful humors that lurked just below the surface of his dark mind.

He knew there was nothing to be done for it, and either way, he barely slept at all, fevers and pains turning his nights into torture, and all he could do was drink and rage and drink again to dull it. Though even when awake, the dreams came to him, the raids, the battles, the blood and the triumphs. Then the fall, and it all fell to pieces, their horde ripped apart by squabbling rats calling themselves war chiefs and claiming the right to lead. His days of fighting seemed to be done, his strong arm no longer able to draw or hold the blade he loved so.

A tap on his shoulder, the drunkard passing the skin back to him, and he grasped it awkwardly. Another grunt escaped him, and the harsh drink burned with some pleasure as he swallowed, before passing it back, his eyes and mind fixed far away, deep in the mists drifting across the marshes. Perhaps he could still fight, given the time. His weak arm had held a shield at need, and he was damned if he would let the fevers take him. Losing an arm, even the strong one, did not need to mean the end to his fighting days, and he would make up for skill with all the anger that still roiled within him. Gamiczh tugged his furs closer around him and settled in for the watch.

The Blind

Zhrylli had lost her sight the same day she had lost her mate and chieftain. The cravens had come in the night, long cruel blades stabbing and tearing, and it had torn her asunder to see him ripped apart. When she came to, she was beaten and bloody, dragged out to be shared as just another part of the spoils, the other wives having already been given to new masters. She had been a fool of a girl, although a fool with pride and strength enough not to accept this lot, but her attempt at escape had been futile, and so they had taken her eyes with burning irons, leaving only searing sores.

They had all turned her away, none would have a half-mad cripple, and so she was given a place among the unfit, those who could not raid or fight, and left to serve those who had taken such riches from her own downfall. She had seethed and raged, but even infernos die down, and in the smoldering ashes she nurtured a glowing ember that fueled her. She learned patience, she learned the songs. The histories would in time pass to her, and before long, the chieftain's first wife had become remade as the Crone, and as she took her place amongst the elders of the tribe, her voice gained strength.

With the passing of the Golden Eyed, the last of her betrayers had been felled, and in their desperation the tribe had turned to the wisest of the voices that remained to them, and even those who now squabbled for the tattered reins of power would bow to her words, she was sure of it. Her word was to travel north, into the lands they had raided and hunted when she herself had been in the folly of her youth. She would feel the winds of the grey crags again, make herself a throne and see her tribe brought back to strength in time. The deep places of the mountains would be their cradle. And then she would find a good ending, some way to bring her own song to a thundering conclusion.

The Mad

Ghall had seen them prancing onto the field of glory, banners rippling in the wind, armor shining and singing a clanging song of battle. Ever since it had been all he could think of, all he could speak of, all he wanted. But goblins cannot be knights, that's what they all said. Goblins know nothing of honor, nothing of bravery or chivalrous deeds. But Hoqx paid them no heed. There were many things he did not know, the meaning of any of those words for one, but that would not stop him from his noble quest. Already he had assembled a metal skin from the leavings he had scrounged from the battlefield, and now all he needed was a mighty steed and he could go forth and do the great deeds that awaited him.

The Risen

On! Onwards! Always onwards they went, for they must move to live, to find new lands to raid, to hunt, to grow. The calling had been sudden, a fevered dream from a poisoned wound that all swore would kill him. Yet, on the fourth day **Pzelloch** had thrown aside the healing hands of the old Whisperer, choosing the fire rather than the stinking poultices to heal his wounds, and ever since he had driven them on, always with an eye to the horizon.

The warband had grown since leaving the barren hills of their homes and venturing through the hinterlands. Smaller bands had joined them, some of free will, some after the persuasion of cold hard iron, but by one path or the other they put aside their feuds and hatred and swore their blades and blood to the cause. The pain was with him still, a mellow throbbing that pushed him ever on, always at the front, always in the eyes of his people. Whenever his eyes would close he could see the dream anew, as clear as it had been that night. A thousand tribes, and a thousand banners, their war cries shaking the skies themselves, and a mountain bathed in blood.

The Banners

The first they saw was a cloud rising out of the horizon, a storm of riotous banners coming out of the steppes, borne aloft by the victorious heroes, fresh from the field. Those who looked out from the high walls of Sarn Qorn began the call, and before the sun was high in the sky the battlements were brimming with those who had been praying for the safe return of the army. One by one, the banners became legible to the eyes on the battlements, and happy shouts went out on the wind to greet the heroes on their return. Before long, the banners of the city went up in answer, and the city made ready for a feast.

One by one, they bore forth from the gates, first the companies of the city, their colors catching the wind and lighting up in front of the walls. After them came the guests, their own colors adding themselves to the bustling array of welcome. They formed ranks to either side of the gate, a path down which a smaller procession rode, a great banner of gold and silver cloth in patterns around the scroll of the city, and the court and attendants following on foot. Before the banner rode the Great Reader himself, seeming to the world as a man chiseled in stone, a stone face covering a man whose heart was breaking and soaring in turns.

Atop the high tower above the gate, a small figure looked out, her young eyes scanning the banners nearing the walls, looking from one to the other in a nervous search for a serpent slithering amongst the silks. It seemed an age since she had stood up there last, seeing three riders disappearing into the hills, and now she was desperate to know that the waiting had not been in vain, that the hope and the silent word whispered into the dark nights had not been simple self-torture.

Omrakish

The handsome young general of the house of Tonopol had been given the honor of the vanguard, leading his jubilant warriors in a procession towards the waiting crowd. They were fewer than when they set out, having left many of their brothers in a ceremonial grave near the field where they had fallen.

He had been at the center of the fighting and had led his men into the very heart of the grey-skin throng once his overlord had brought the heavy horses into the charge. They had met in the thick of it, Omrakish's men fighting like demons on all sides, driving the panicking enemies away from their beloved general.

After the battle, he had been honored in front of the whole army, and Tirsander himself had taken him by the hand and raised it aloft for all to see. He had called him champion and named him the Red Eagle for his ferocious action, his talons still dripping.

Tirsander

The marching column of soldiers halted at a loud, trumpeted command, and the lone figure of the young general rode forth into the empty space that still separated the armies. The cheers and salutations boomed out from the city, and Omrakish basked in the glory for a long moment before he threw his hands up, inviting a silence.

His voice had been made strong and harsh by the bellowing of battle, but there was no hiding the evident joy in him as he proclaimed the victory to the renewed cheers from the crowds, watching from on high. As silence came anew, he could hardly contain his excitement in the next announcement.

"He swept our enemies before us! A vengeful bolt of righteous thunder!" He indicated the court, and the Reader himself, "My liege! His glory is a reflection of your own. I give you your general, Tirsander!"

At a single sweep of his hand, the army split down the middle, making a broad way. Twelve riders stood but only the leader rode forth, his armor polished and gleaming, his great war banner a blur behind him. Battle had shed years from him, and Tirsander was a man reborn.

The deafening roar of the city continued unabated, a wild show of appreciation for their beloved champion in his display, and the Reader stepped forth to embrace his brother and first and foremost of his generals. As they broke apart grinning as only brothers can, the elder noticed the twinkle of mischief in his younger brother's eye but had no time to ask.

The retinue of the general had caught up, each carrying the banners of their companies, and Tirsander took a step to the side, beckoning forth the slightest of the mounted figures. Sliding from the saddle, the heavy silk flapped gently with each step as the distance closed, and the general looked back to his liege.

"She truly is your daughter, sire, through and a thousand times through."

With half her hair hacked off, Ayaan's silhouette had not been the one her father had been looking for among the soldiers, and so the shock was sudden, and obvious, when she stood before him, every inch the warrior. His breath caught in his throat as he fought down the sudden rush of emotions, and Ayaan, proving her uncle right, went to embrace him, speaking words none could hear over the tumult of the crowd.

Ayaan

In his face was written the agony of fear and the dread of loss, the lines of his face more drawn than when she had left, and she knew the cause. Her father had always been one to worry, in all facets of his life, and while it made him a great leader of his city and his people, as a father it caused him no end of, well, worry.

His hands were the same smooth, gentle hands they had always been, and the touch brought her back home, back to the beginning, back to being the daughter, as he was the father, back to the way it had been. But it was but a comforting lie, and she could tell by his face that he was aware of the change in her, and that it was breaking his heart. And still he was fighting back his sentimentalities, not wanting it to obscure his pride in her and the joy of her return. She loved him for that.

Nodding to his brother, he leaned in close and with the tone he would have used when her younger self was caught raiding the kitchens or sneaking out after dark he managed, "Little desert djinn, what mischief have you managed?"

Mellie and Blue

The peace of late autumn was settling in, with so many fleeing south for the winter, and so many others gathering what would be needed for the long sleep. The forest was a place of silence now, broken by the odd song from those who were set to stay the cold watch and greet spring's warming rays once it came around.

Blue was one of them, a stubborn bird who was not about to be ordered. And since not even winter seemed to be about to force a change in her friend's mind, the young pixie was not about to try. The burrow would be that much cozier for the company, and the long nights would pass in song and cheer.

It was the squirrels and the mice that had taught her the best places to find seeds and nuts, how best to store them, and how to make them taste their best, and her larder was now heaped with everything **Mellie** had gathered. As thanks, she would use the last of that good salt in preparing for the feast, and after that, they would all settle in to sleep, and she would watch the world turn white, and begin the wait. She was glad Blue was stubborn; the wait would be easier with a friend.

It wasn't the cold that drove them inside, it was still not the frozen season quite yet, but the wind and the wet made bitter allies of the chill and so **Blue** had suggested they get into the warm shelter of the burrow. That is to say Blue scampered off inside and chirped happily about the comforts of the little den until the little pixie came along.

Soon there could be heard singing coming from the opening to the burrow, along with an occasional glimpse of light that escaped from between the moss hangings, little signals to the world that life went on, and even through the cold time, there would be song in the forest.

"Sing, sweet minstrel, of sleep and dreams
The world, for now is sleeping.
Sing, little minstrel, of rivers and streams
Of water once more streaming.

Soon the great rest will cover the land
Just you and me and the forest
Seeing the white cover mountain to strand
But we'll be warm in this nest.

So sing sweet minstrel of spring anew
The world will wake from dreaming
Bring back the singers, from whence they flew
And the sun once more will be beaming"

They sung well together, far into the long hours of the night, keeping the dark at bay, their songs a bulwark against the winter.

The snow had come in the night, rendering the dark hours a bright downpour of large pillows of the stuff, and by morning it covered everything, while slowly turning into little streams and puddles as the sun rose into the sky.

Blue was first out of the burrow, happily hopping around, marveling at the pretty prints she could leave behind her and testing the cushioning effect of the stuff by leaping into any heap in sight and sending the fresh snow skywards once again.

The clouds of the night had all but passed, and for all the heralds of winter, it was pleasant out, the warming rays glinting off her bells as she hoisted them onto her shoulders. They would make for the Old Oak, and the Gathering. All would be there, a last bright feast before the sleep.

When the Blue Vein Mines were abandoned over a hundred years past, much was left behind as the resident dwarves fled the plague that had decimated them. All that they could not carry away with them had to be left, including the vast spoils of their excavations.

The **grey-skins** that eventually made it their stronghold were not craftsmen, and so knew nothing of the making and purification of fine metals, but would make good use of the scraps and leavings to fashion themselves crude helmets and suits of armor, binding and beating, bolting and bending where they had no skill in welding and forging.

The horde, now spewing forth from the deep, carried the spawn of what had been so long in the making. The clamor of their march was terrible to behold, a dark, heavy stain, bleeding out of the old gates, the battlements the defiled tumble-down remnants of those who soon shall again be beleaguered.

Wrecker

He was the product of a life spent scraping his way to the top of the pile, every step a bloody struggle, every underling a foe beaten into accepting him as chief, as warlord.

In the dark he had prepared, binding his horde with oaths and vows as hard as the iron he had used to make them a fierce, bristling terror to be unleashed at his will. Now he would use them as a great, iron hammer to crush those bearded bastards, and whoever chose to stand with them.

Of all the brutes and bullies that had come up and beaten their bloody way to the fore of a grey-skin throng, none had ever been more dangerous, more cruel, more bloodthirsty than this one, none more single-minded in their hunger to destroy, rather than raid. And now he had come forth at last.

High above the broken fort, huddled amongst the rocks, a pair of sharp eyes flickered back and forth across the dark, clamorous stain spreading from the blackened ruins that had once been the gates of a proud realm.

With each banner counted he bit another notch into a stalk, trying for some rough idea of the numbers that were spewing forth from the mountain, his initial curiosity turning ever grimmer as the valley began to fill with the horde.

The sun was westering, the glare making him squint as he saw the last of the banners trickle out to join the horde. He sighed to himself, shaking his head in despair. There was no knowing a clear number, and in these barren hills he could not risk a closer look, but even at his most optimistic, the spawn of the deep was beyond anything his master had feared.

Mickel could smell it on the wind. Under the smell of his travelling companions struggling up the hill after him, sticking out from the scents of the creatures hidden by the snow, and the fragrance of dead leaves and sleeping plants, it was there, at the edge of sensing. A stink, some foul, rotten odor carried up from the south.

He had bounded on ahead of the others, their band having grown to half a dozen riders now, Birker's friends having come along for the next leg of the journey, something that to Mickel simply meant far greater opportunities for treats and delicious bones to rip apart.

Where they were going and why seldom troubled him; he left such worries up to Birker, though his worries seemed to be weighing on him far heavier as of late, his mind seeming to drift in deep thoughts whenever Mickel curled up in his lap to be rubbed and petted. It must be something to do with where they were going, and perhaps this new smell was part of it, as well.

Birker

There was a grim aspect to him as they ascended the hill, Hedda making light of the struggle. The heavy iron of the mail and braces were reminders of a time and a duty he had tried to leave behind, a part of him he had somehow known he would never be rid of.

The others were keeping up a low chatter behind them, and the sweet scents from their pipes would have usually had Birker lighting his own and taking a part in those debates that were as much a part of any travelling fellowship as were the endless miles. Still, **Birker** kept ahead, his eyes picking out old markers he knew from a lifetime ago.

There was no putting words to his worries, but by some sense or another, he knew something was off. By all his craft of tracking and trailing, he could only find traces of old leavings from the age-old enemy, tracks long cold, squats long abandoned. While he was perfectly happy not having to deal with them, they could not simply have vanished. They must have gone somewhere...

It rose out of the crags, a simple-looking tower house, seeming oddly small for the gate it overlooked. **Birker** smiled in spite of himself, knowing the deception and the many traps that made the approach a death trap for any would-be attacker.

The others were already descending into the defile that led up to the gate, but the trio held back, and looking down he could tell he was not the only one who was not overly thrilled to be back. Mickel, always one to be first into the warmth and comfort of any shelter was fast by his heel, giving out a drawn, peevish whine.

"Never meant for us to come back this way you know." He shifted in the saddle and let Mickel scurry up before him, tucking himself in under a fold of the cape. Birker spat, as if to ward something off and sighed, "Well, no good waiting out here till we lose the light, let's get this reunion over with."

The great gates barely had time to rumble shut behind him before Birker began regretting his return. They were greeted by stewards who made to take their mounts off to be brushed and fed, and **Birker** made a point of ordering that Hedda be given both carrots and apples with her hay, and he made a note to himself to sneak out a tankard of ale for her later. She deserved a few treats.

They were greeted with the lively dancing fires of the Hearth Hall, its namesake running down the length of the massive stone room, the heat rising off the logs making the air blur, and the smell of the roasting meats making the newly arrivals water at the mouth. The rest were shown to places at the long table, seated with the dwarves of the garrison, but Birker was shown in through a door and down a tunnel he had walked a hundred times before.

The commander's quarters were much the same as they had been last he was there, and so to was the old, scowling dwarf who broke from the huddled group around the map table and ran an eye over Birker.

The Old Wolf of the Grey Guard had a voice like stone on metal, an angry rasp. "Ah, so it was true as the missive said then, the Goat walks among us once more...and what is more, he wears his own feed now?"

What would have been a chuckle in any other, came out as a croaking growl. It was the closest thing he ever came to mirth.

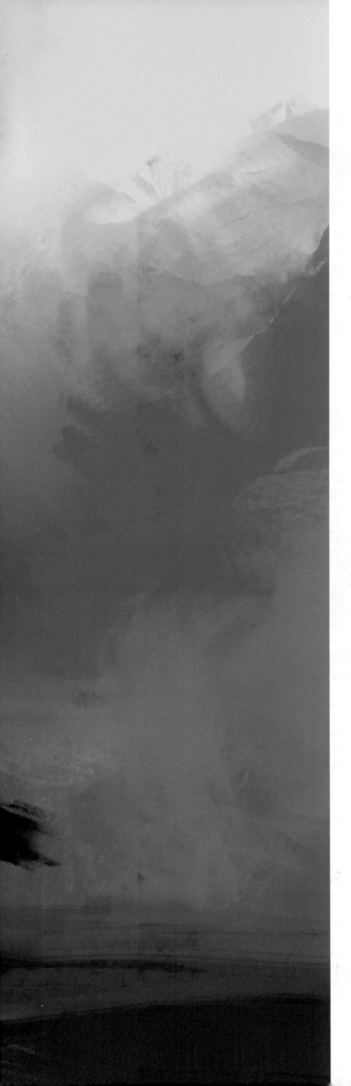

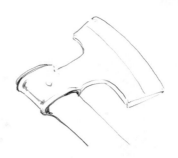

"So, this is the one who spins tales of the gathering storm, is it?" The tone was gruff, but not as cruel as that of the Old Wolf and came from the youngest of the figures gathered around the map table. He looked **Birker** up and down with a measuring eye, and it was hard to tell his thoughts on what he saw. An answer seemed expected, and Birker had to fight to stop himself from bristling at the impudent tone of a youngling unaware of the rank still due to him, in spite of his long absence.

"Introduce yerself before snarlin', welp, you address one who has more battles in his past than you have heard tales of. This toothy old gremlin might not have had the thought to tell you, but you shall soon enough know to whom ye speak."

To his delight Birker saw both the young and the old redden, one from embarrassment, the other from rage, but before either could speak, Birker went on, "Don't bother yerself, I don't come as unprepared as some. I know of you, Thorgal of the Kyrn Mordun; the Black Hammer they call you."

A hand slammed on the table, and the mounting babble subsided as they all looked in silence at the one glowering over the maps at them all as a deep booming voice rolled out into the room hazed in a puff of fragrant smoke.

"Enemies gather, a menace grows, the likes of which we have not seen for long years, or so you say, and still you fight like children."

The speaker was the eldest present, one who had held command even when the Old Wolf was young. He was the Hornblower now, a position of high regard in all the companies of the guard, and only given to those of ancient standing in their order. His eyes flashed dangerously as his gaze raked them, and they all stood back abashed as he took another deep pull at his pipe. "Now, I don't imagine the White Ram returns here lightly, and if my eyes are still to be trusted, there is at least one story he can tell that will be worth hearing."

Birker nodded gratefully to the elder dwarf, walked to the table, and they all gathered around, suddenly curious as young beardlings to hear the tale.

They shrieked and cawed as they came in, hundreds of her children, her servants, her eyes. The dark wings blotted out the moon as they filled the night with their sightings, and with each she conversed, knitting together the happenings of the world in her mind's eye, and her dread grew as the tidings darkened. Yet there was hope, and still some time in which to aid those who would resist the tide that darkened the horizon, and soon as many birds were flying off on new errands as were arriving from their distant postings. The small gods must be roused out of their idle isolations, having left the doings of the world to their greater cousins and the mere mortals who must suffer their whims.

Soon all but three of her aides had taken wings, the finest of her murder, and to each she spoke in turn, for they must find her three most powerful allies of old and call upon them to fulfill a promise they had made long years ago. It was a debt she did not want to give up, but it was to throw what power **she who watches** had into the fray and lend her weight to the fulcrum that would decide the future.

He had known the message even before the black-clad messenger had exclaimed his first squawk. He had been suspicious ever since his sons had escorted the dwarf and his companions to the ends of their lands, ever since his overlord had set the pieces moving. For himself, **Fercindur** had wanted to stay clear, to keep his pack close and keep their own lands safe, but old debts must out. It was, in fact, due to his sons that he found himself beholden to the wishes of the feathered one, and for the service she had done him he knew it was fair to ask his return to the great game, to have him and his play their part.

A growl exploded from him, taking the raven's pontification in the middle of a sentence and stopping it dead. He might be bound by debt and honor, but he had had enough of listening to the flying rat.

"Fercindur's folk will come, now be away from my court and my lands, and fly back to your mother."

The herald needed no prompting and took to the air at once. For a long while the king went on in quiet thought, the future now seeming so close, so pressing. The howl was long and strong, summoning all of the blood. Only to those in his confidence was the faint edge of melancholic sadness evident, and reflected in their answering song.

121

The Princess

The black herald had been welcomed and flattered, fed and feasted, in the hope that they might make him forget his errand and be well on his way before recalling why his wings had borne him all this way to begin with. But in spite of their best efforts, the crow did not relent in his mission, always bringing the talk back to the pressing words he brought from She Who Watches, and after long and long after that again, **the Princess of White** sighed; she knew her freedom must have a cost. It was time to pay.

"That which has been asked shall be granted, and tell your darling mother I shall call on her after all this unpleasantness is done. It has been too long."

She made a courtly bow, which was returned by the young herald, and they made their goodbyes. Once the beating of his wings had receded, she let the glamour fall away, and the glade returned to being as pristine and white as if no one had ever disturbed the trees.

"Come, Ursul," she said mounting, "we have some friends to see."

The High Kin

Up, up, forever up, climbing from perch to perch, up past where the trees quit, and further, to where the snows lay even in summer. Into valleys and over peaks there laid the silent protectors of the recipients of the last message.

Ever since the sundering they had tired of the world, seeing their strength and kin bleeding away to settle in distant lands and lose the old ways. They had retreated, taking all their wisdom, learning, and beauty and taking refuge in a bastion hidden away from the world.

Few are those who ever find their way here, and fewer still are those who leave, for those who guard the secret vale and the High Hold are jealous in their duties, and do not trust to friendships as they would have of old.

Yet, the voices of gods have a long reach, and borne on the black wings, they can reach far indeed.

The Woodkin

The Woodkin are the finest of warriors, fighters with few equals, relentless in their pursuits of duty, of skill, and of improvement. Once they take the field, gathered under a banner, and in the service of a single purpose, there are few things that can hope to be of effective opposition.

Yet, they are seldom seen gathered, and then almost never has there been sightings of them in large numbers marching abroad, seeing little reason to fight for those who dwell beyond the Deep Woods, for the Woodkin are warriors who fight of their own volition, for their own reasons. They are not soldiers.

Yet they had come together, in numbers greater than any time before, and had, through trials of wits and combat elected one to lead them. To him they had all sworn their blood and their blades, taking oaths to him and to each other of friendship and protection. They were gathered, they marched, and with them, the promise of great deeds and greater songs.

No two ever looked the same, even if they all shared the armor of living wood, for the growers shape themselves to the needs of the warriors, and each of them fights with different prowess. Some will fight up close, some from afar, some grow a carapace of woven woodwork for their protection, while others use their growers to enhance their strengths.

When battle is joined, it is not done so in the manner of men, who fight shoulder to shoulder, seeking their safety and power in numbers, fighting panic as often as they fight the enemy. Nor do they fight with the unity of dwarves, who will form and move as large formations with singular purpose.

When the warriors of the Deep Woods come to the fore, it is with a fluidity born from a shared mind, where each of them knows where every other is. They move as a wave, each of them fighting a handful of enemies at any given time, but never alone, always with the help of their **Blade Bretheren**.

He was not of the Ancients, having never had a seat with their council nor a seat of his own. A younger son of a greater house, he had demanded the right to stand in the trial for command and though it had nearly cost him his life, his was the only blade undefeated at the end of the last bout.

His return, his journeys the year before had caused some stir within the princedoms of the Greenlands, his travels having taken him far afield, keeping him from hearth and home for nearly two decades. As he made his tour around the seats of the great houses, he told tales, both grand and dark, of the news from without, and the excitement he had found in the young and impetuous accounted for many of the blades that had come to the cause. Though the glory and pride were not entirely lost on him, it was a melancholy that had most keenly changed the young commander, his usual light manner traded for a stern and focused intensity he brought to every matter concerning what was to come. The glory and pride were somewhat tarnished by the weight he bore, that of each of the lives put into his trust, each loss he would have to account for.

Ragnhild

The young gelding was spirited, and she had to hold on for dear life as it made blurs of the trees as they passed, the wind turning the gentle rain to lashing whip strokes across her cheeks as they tore along, the thundering of their pursuers growing ever nearer.

Thorben had taken one of the long spears through the chest, the fool having thought himself strong enough to hold off the riders until the rest of their party could get away. In spite of his size, he had been ridden into the dirt, the hooves finishing what a lance through his broad chest had not managed.

The ritters, or knights, or champions, the peacocks had many names, they rode horses far stronger and fiercer than the beasts her own party had stolen ahead of the raid, but their burdens were clad in iron and silks, capes and scales from top to toe, and so they tired with the miles. But they were stubborn, and though their shouts of abuse had gone, their pursuit seemed determined, and Ragnhild clenched her jaw.

Younger sons of lesser houses, those with the means to maintain a retinue but with no seat of their own, with a hunger for renown and respected service, and perhaps the chance to earn a place at court, these often took the king's coin and added themselves to the Knights of the Law.

These paladins of justice travelled the kingdom, keeping the king's peace, gathering militias when bandits needed sorting out, and dispensed intelligence to the court of the goings-on of the lands they meant to govern.

It was not the first time he had killed, but the man had kept fighting, even after the lance had taken him full in the chest, almost as if driven by rage alone. Even after hard killing, his blood was up, and his friends were with him, whooping and shouting as they closed the distance. The horse thieves had been quick and clever, and half the horses of the town had been taken before the alarm was raised, but clever and quick did not in themselves make for good riders, not like those all around him, masters of the horse, one and all.

When she recognized the marks carved into the tree she urged the horse on, one last burst of speed to give her some breathing room. They plunged into the clearing, hazy with the dust kicked up by the passing of a score of horses, and she turned, bringing her sword around to face her pursuers as they made the glade. They halted, each of them at the ready, slowly walking their horses into the clearing, spreading out so as to attack her from every angle. Her horse made to back away, but she forced him around while keeping all eyes on her. One of the riders trotted forwards, his sword leveled at her, his weight perfectly balanced for the strike.

"We have you, horse thief, and soon enough we shall have the rest of your band!" There was challenge in his tone, as well as triumph.

Ragnhild grinned and nodded, "Why don't I introduce you right away?"

The confusion passed like a shadow across the man's face, and then there was panic there.

On the shouted "UP!" the forest floor erupted with armed men, all bristling with the layers of undergrowth, old grass, and leaves that had kept them hidden for the hours of waiting. They were all armed with axes and spears, some even with the heavy lengths of iron that served these northerners for swords, and in an instant, they had a half a hundred dark gleaming spearheads leveled at the riders.

A hand held up was all the signaling his companions needed to know his orders, and their lances were dropped to the ground with some hesitance, and at a word from the one on the gelding, men were among them, taking their swords and daggers, and Baldain felt a keen loss as his own sword was taken from him. He swore a silent oath that he would win it back, come what may. The spell of his fury was somewhat broken once their captors erupted in cheers and laughter.

Once they were unhorsed and been unburdened of their finer pieces of armor and bound securely, the leader of the band came to them, grinning like a boy who has just managed a magnificent piece of mischief.

"Now, boys! I will not keep you for much longer, the day is getting on, and my friends and I have taken a far better prize than we had expected. However, these are not our lands, and we might need a guide..." he gestured to his men, and they grabbed Baldain by the feet and dragged him off, kicking and protesting. When his friends joined in the shouted abuse, their captor rounded on them, his spear tight in his hand.

"Now I have dealt fairly with you boys, and I wish not to shed blood of mere children..." The sneer was as broad and cunning as that of a fox.

Grey-Skins

What drives them on, what fuels their hatred and their lust for vengeance? It took them two weeks to overcome the defences, the bitter defeat fought by monks, old and young, armed with bows first, and then hewing axes and long kitchen knives.

It had not saved them; every last one had been put to a blade. It had been a stalwart fortress to the godly, now it was a smoldering ruin, and the horde passed on, fattened on the flesh of the vanquished. The chief drove them north and west, against the mounting winter wind. Before them were rich hunting grounds, behind they left a scorched, blackened nothing.

Inside he could feel it growing, something deep, deep down, something from time before time. An ancient voice speaking words he could not make out. But he knew how to appease it, how to do its bidding, and in turn, it would grant him power. The promise of power...it was the fuel that drove them all.

Strength is the only order they bow to, and only then to have the blows and kicks directed at someone else. The horde is a roiling hive of climbers, all reaching over the dead and discarded they have torn down to climb another rung, to gain another foothold.

Their only crafts are raids and ruin; they create nothing, except what they can clobber together from the remnants of their loot, making bloody rags of the riches that stood before their coming, and only death in their wake.

Before the dark mass of the horde fled both man and beast, whole towns had been abandoned when they knew they were in the path of the age-old enemy, and so the horde grew restless with no one to fight but each other. They needed a challenger...

Frostbreds

The wind whispered to them, a gentle song among the howls that haunted the snowclad expanses of the mountain ranges. It chorused of a dark tide, and the storm for which it was the harbinger, a terrible crash that was not theirs to weather.

The Old Men of the Mountains held with no banner, owed no allegiance. They had both fought and befriended most of those who shared their mountains, but they wished no part in the squabbles of the littlelings. To them it mattered little who claimed to rule the stone halls or the lowlands; they would never make it out in the freedom of the high places.

There had been a time when they would not have suffered trespassers, when they would have driven them off, as in the songs. They had been many once, and their power would have driven off even the strongest invader, but the ages had weakened them and taken many of their numbers. And age had given them wisdom and patience, and the knowing that the mountains could defeat all.

It was a rhythm, a catching tune, each step to an order, as if the dance had been done a hundred times over, and where before there had been anger, fear, and hatred, now there was elation, and there was the dance.

Carŷa had not thought to draw the blade, and in truth had no memory of loosening the cloth she had used to strap it to her back, only the feeling of the handle in her grasp, the whispered urging and the blade shedding its weight as she tested it.

It must have been after her dagger stuck deep in one man's leg she remembered that. Her sword she had seen lodged in another man's belly, he staggering back to crash into his friends. Then the tune, the rhythm, and the dance.

There was sweetness in the silence that followed as the sword sunk smoothly into the last man, pinning his corpse to the ground as the last of his life welled out of him. She sunk to one knee and the dance came to an end.

It was new, this feeling of joy in the slaughter. It had nothing to do with the ending of life, the shedding of blood or with the violence visited on those who stood in her path, nothing of what warriors will sing of. The joy was in the finding, the discovery of a voice in harmony with her own, someone new to dance with.

Carÿa thought he would have been there, the sweet-smelling elf. His smirk still irked her, and she had been looking forward to wiping it off him as she took his money, but now she was not so sure. This dance, this voice, this silken whisper, it stole away the glint of the gold. What else could ever be so sweet...?

The Hidden People

The king and the herald had walked the gardens for the better part of the day, and with every step, with every hour passed, with every word traded, the king's mood darkened. His kingdom was a jewel-bright remnant of the greatness that had once been, a relic of a time when the world had come to bend the knee at his father's court. Left to him was the safeguarding of that which they had salvaged from the ashes, kept hidden by their own craft, and the aid of she who now sent for his.

"You ask of me to send forth my champions, to risk them against this storm, and for what? Here we are protected, the menace of these lowly beings cannot reach us here," he sighed, and looked out across the vale, the last refuge of his kin. "You ask me to risk it for a fight not our own."

The herald cawed loudly, as if to emphasize his response, "Sire! We ask of you merely that which is your own heart's dearest desire. We ask you to walk the path of your forefathers, to make the world recall the greatness that once was!"

The weight of the armor had the familiarity of an old friendship, lost for too long, a sweet reunion. The silver gleam of the solid feathers reflected the light of the early morning sky, the sun still a faint promise of pink on the horizon. Their like had not taken to the field for an age, though their prowess reflected in those who had carried on their learning. Their woodland kin still remembered, though even to them there were secrets they did not know.

The king looked around, his champions the resplendent image of the heroes of old. Sagas had been made of lesser warriors, each of them the proud keeper of the old flame, each a son to him, each the equal of any king. The sight filled him with a boundless pride, his longing for a time near forgotten fulfilled in them. Yet sadness there was also, for in them was made clear to him how precious few were left of them, and keener again was made the anguish of knowing they might well be riding forth to their doom, and the diminishing of all he held dear. This was the cursed power of kingship, to be able to change the world, and the knowledge of what that truly meant.

The Blackbirds

The new recruits were shaping up better than she had expected, though most of them would still need winter in encampment to make proper **Blackbirds**. The drills were doing their work though, and most now could follow orders as they were given.

They had filled the ranks at the mustering, even taking on a few extra young ones for runner duties and other lesser work. In a few seasons, they too would be offered a proper place in the company. When spring broke, their company would be whole again, and she knew that the harder she pushed them now, the closer they would all be once the word came down to march to the front.

The workshops of the hold were running night and day now as more and more of the guards were streaming in, every company answering the call, and the smithies would have to provide. They all brought the arms and gear particular to their companies, but now they would be fitted for war.

Most companies, being used to ranging the high passes of the mountains and the hills and vales that made up their lands, carried at most vests and shirts of mail, sturdy enough, but little compared to the likes of the armory of the Kyrn.

Birker's own axe had been given over for some much-needed reworking by the master of the forge, who had grimaced at seeing the harsh marks that heavy use and rough living had left on the fine weapon. He had given Birker a sour look, as if he had insulted his dear mother, and said he would send for the commander when the damage was undone.

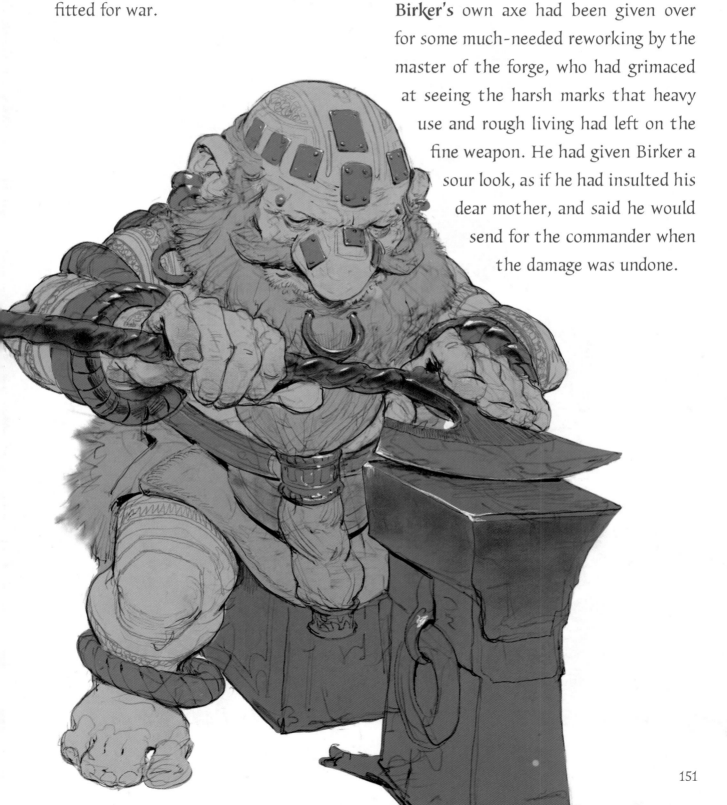

They came up the causeway on the eighth day, not a company of the guard, but a mustering of the hearthcarls that made up the garrison of most of the local clans. **Birker**, having been summoned by the blaring bronze horns, went out to meet them, these veterans from a time before the forming of the guard, when the clans would just as soon fight each other as make common cause.

Each and every one was a greybeard, old and hard as the mountains they defended, each sworn to a service that now denied them what they all loved even more than gold, more than stout ale, even more than good iron - a battle, and a chance for a death worthy of song.

"You didn't think we were about t'let you smooth cheeked younglings march off without us, did you?" Birker made to answer, but the thumping of fist on chest cut him off.

"Mustering your errand boys is all well and good, but it is best you let us show you how proper fighting is done," and as he saw he was not to be interrupted he nodded to bird cawing on his shoulder and added, "If the tale this one tells is true, we didn't get all dressed up for nothing either. Should be fun."

In the tumultuous bustle of the hold, **Birker** found peace in the stables where he finally made good on his promise to Hedda. The stout fragrant ale ran dark and sweet, and goat and fox alike seemed to approve immensely of the treat. The clouds had come down to lay as a glittering coat of frost over the mountains, and apart from a backdrop of the muffled revelries of the great hall, all was quiet, the first stillness they had felt in a long while.

The old unease was back in him; he knew he was taking them into danger, but as much as he knew he ought to leave them behind, it was not his choice to make. They had come with him through flight and fight, and he knew the betrayal of abandoning them now, to take away from them the choice to stay or go. Even if they were headed to their ends, they would walk it together, their paths made one by the binding of their friendship.

Mellie and Blue

When all the drink was gone, when all the food was done, when speeches had been spoken, and the gifts and tokens given and received, they gathered for the height of the celebration.

The sun had barely shown itself on that day, skirting the horizon for hours, gracing the sky with shades of amber and dark wine before darkness once again claimed its hold. The dance was a joyous defiance, a raucous stand against the cold and the black that carried them all in heedless throws around and around the bonfires.

To oppose the dark might be a fool's errand for every fire goes out in the end, yet what glorious fools they were. Their slow defeat would be fought, again and again, until darkness was defeated, or they could fight no more.

The darkness had beaten a hasty retreat, but soon enough the dreary dim would return and before the light was all gone they would have to make their way homewards.

It was the red runner of the forest who offered to take them along, four feet being fleeter than two, and in return they would offer to share their lair and larder, for when it comes to the winter sleep, the more the merrier.

They had been dreading the long trek, not for the trudging and the struggle alone, but the promise of trading the cold miles on foot for a comfortable seat and warm fur made the offer all the more welcome.

They made the forest blur in their passing, flying along the paths and trails under the trees, chasing the last of the light, and in their pursuit, catching the joy and freedom that is the true target of any hunt.

The elation lay in knowing that all they needed to do would be to claim the horizon, and a new world would be theirs, and the presence to know that, the freedom in that fleeting moment, was far more precious. Not for them, the great adventures, the conquests and songs, they had no need for such fickle finery. For them the small adventures, the purity of true friendship, and the joys and comforts of a life spent in the moment.

Ahead of the great forest host went the best of the centaurii, **the pathrunners**; in vast sweeps ahead of the march their patrols scouted and watched, sending messages back as they went, and as the host travelled into the foothills the words became darker.

Small bands of grey-skins were seen streaming off into the badlands, no doubt to join themselves to the threat that even now came closer, and as they harried and skirmished with them, those they captured let slip tales of the ways of the encroaching enemy.

Their numbers were hard to determine, but those of the pathrunners that went out for days at a time returned telling of cities sacked, of whole forests burned, of sludge and boglands made of the lakes that had been before. Those hill tribes that still counted the elves as foes had gone to join the horde of grey, and there were even sightings of the Weeper and his host of ogres among their ranks now.

The grey-skins had learned, if slowly, not to give chase, even when the long arrows raked their ranks and some fell, never again to rise. The ogres had never learned the lesson, and stung by the vicious barbs of the runners, they trundled after.

Flight after flight would add to the burning rage that drove them on, added to by teasing taunts and songs. Try as they might, the furious slashes and swings never hit as they were meant, but merely blunted their great axes and cleavers.

Before long they were lost to the sight of the horde, and the woodlands themselves became a combatant, slowly sapping the great brutes of their strength, and had them gasping and heaving in the thick forest air.

The cruel cunning of the Keeper's capture was what it stole away from the victim. The ogre had spent its fury breaking through the barricades of foliage and bracken in its headlong chase, and once it understood the danger it was already too late. The coiling branches and roots had hold and would not let go.

Before long there was only the face left, not being slowly strangled, and the young general could stand atop the vanquished foe to see the fearsome kin that made common cause with the enemy.

Nothing was ever so pathetic as the impotent bellowing roars, the heedless defiance that betrayed the emptiness of their bravery. They charged wild and blind into battle, not grave, but too stupid to know fear. Looking down into the hateful eyes, he felt no sadness at what had to be done.

Birker

It had taken most of the night, and the grey light of dawn was only lending its softest caress to the sky as **Birker** emerged from the armory. Has tattoos had faded and withered, and so they had been renewed as his armor had been fitted.

The armorers had made a fitting piece of work of his harness, and the helmet they gave him was a masterpiece, the two great horns lending an aspect of terror to the mask of battle.

It had been more than an age of men since last he had held the mantle that he had left behind when he quit the guard, and he had never thought it likely he would resume wearing it. As he crossed the yard towards the stables however, he found himself humming an old marching song, and he felt the familiar giddiness come over him. The White Bock would march once again.

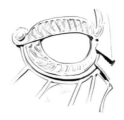

They marched at first light. All eight companies, a full legion of dwarves, all armored, all filthy and ready for what they knew was to come. Even Mickel had been fitted with a small shirt of mail, and the smiths, no slouches they, had made a new head piece for Hedda.

It was an old feeling made anew, being at the head of a host that followed him, in part for duty, in part for glory, and in part for the knowing that great songs would be sung of their exploits.

Seeing such a mustering of his people, it had not been in the world for time untold, and it stirred something in him, something he had kept deep inside, hidden away next to his vanity. Now he let it stir for a little, feeling like a warming draft of the copper kettles.

Henrik Rosenborg

Ayse Irem Aktas

Pauline Voß

Paul Dainton

Robbie Trevino

Manuel Castañón

Jana Schirmer

Additional
Art

TEGN – Book Three

366 days, 366 sketches telling 366 stories, some smaller, some greater.

Shared with the community, fi rst online, and now as a series of books: TEGN - Book Three is the last of three books featuring the journeys and stories that came about as the result of a decision on the first day of 2016: "draw something today, and the next day and the next" and soon the doodles took on a life of their own, summoning up grand adventures and ideas for a world emerging slowly from the mists of imagination.

Even Mehl Amundsen is a freelance concept artist from Norway who has worked for studios like Volta, Blizzard, Riot, Wizards of the Coast and many more. Besides that he has been working on his own world shown in TEGN. He travels a lot, teaching what he has learned in workshops and giving advice to newcomers.

Many thanks to all you who have taken part in the adventure so far, it has been our pleasure to go exploring this little world with you, and we hope our travels have just begun. Wherever the road takes us we hope you will come along, for the road is long, and good companionship is more precious than gold

TEGN – Book Three by Even Mehl Amundsen

ISBN 979-10-96315-20-8

Stories and art: Even Mehl Amundsen
Design: Spiridon Giannakis
Proofreading: Courtney Trowbridge
Co-edited and distributed by Editions Caurette

www.tegn.shop

First Printing, 2018
Made in Germany